TO **AMELIA**

Love from

..........................

"**Eww! What's that?**" Amelia asks,
while pointing at the telly.
"That's plastic rubbish," Mum explains.
"It's horrible and smelly."

So why's it floating everywhere?
How come it's in the sea?
Why are the turtles getting stuck?
They should be **swimming free**!

When plastic was invented,
everybody was amazed.
"What is this awesome stuff?" they said.
It took hold like a craze.

But Amelia knows that plastic's
not the wonder we all thought.
It's **poisoning our planet** and
this message must be taught.

Amelia, the time is now,
to wage a **war on waste**.
Put on that suit and grab your mask,
we really must make haste.

The oceans can do many things,
but they can't clean up this mess.
It's up to us, Amelia.
There are things we must address....

Don't let go of that balloon – it ends up in the sea!

The plastic thrown away each year
could circle the earth **FOUR** times.

**Every minute**, one rubbish truck of plastic is d u m p e d into our oceans.

Almost **half** of the rubbish in the oceans is left behind by fishermen.

An octopus cries, "Amelia!
My legs are stuck in cups.
The oceans contain tonnes of these.
We need to clean them up!"

"When we buy drinks that look like this,
the cups and lids get thrown."
Amelia says, "I know.
I'll tell people: **'BRING YOUR OWN!'**"

A turtle swims past Amelia
with bags caught on his flippers.
"Please help," the little turtle asks,
"I hate these plastic slippers."

"Fruit and veg in plastic bags?
Let's stop this single-use."
Amelia says, "I've got it.
Tell everyone to **'BUY THEM LOOSE!'**"

Amelia swims up to the shore.
"Hi, Crab. What's in your claws?"
The crab frowns back, "I'm cleaning up
this mess of plastic straws."

"The beach is where we live and play.
It's where we go to bed."
Amelia says, "We'll help by using
**PAPER STRAWS** instead."

This dolphin's caught up in a net
and cannot swim about.
Amelia dives back in to save her.
"You poor thing; I'll get you out!"

Amelia asks, "What can we do?
This really needs to stop."
She says, "Tell your fishermen to
**PICK UP EVERYTHING** they drop."

Amelia helps clear up the nets,
the straws, the nasty foam.

Amelia's changing how she acts
to make the oceans better.
She even asks Mum, **"Who's in charge?"**
so she can write a letter.

Amelia says, "We must take action.
There's really no excuse.
To save our underwater friends
we must **reduce our use**!"

Amelia's telling her whole class,
"Change can start with you!"

AMELIA
IS MY
HERO

"Try trading old toys with your mates. **DON'T ALWAYS BUY** things new!"

"I'm Amelia, Guardian of the Seas,
and I will show the way.
I'll fight to **save the oceans** for us,
every single day!"

# Amelia! Become a Plastic Hero!

Tick everything you will (or already!) do to take action against plastic pollution.

Use paper straws (or get a cool reusable straw!) ☐

Don't flush wet wipes down the toilet ☐

Swap toys with my friends instead of asking for new ones ☐

Talk to my family about using less plastic ☐

Carry my food in a lunch box ☐

Make my own snacks ☐

Recycle as much plastic as possible ☐

Tell my friends what I've learned ☐

No littering ☐

Ask everyone to stop using glitter and sequins ☐

Get a reusable water bottle ☐

Hey Amelia, if you can stop using single-use plastic you will make a **BIG** difference!

Amelia, write four things you will tell your friends and family about plastic.

## Amelia's Plastic Pledge

I, Amelia, promise to reduce my plastic use to help save my fishy friends.

Sign here: _____

Date: _____

Written by J.D. Green
Illustrated by Ela Smietanka
Designed by Nicky Scott

First published by HOMETOWN WORLD in 2019
Hometown World Ltd
1 Queen Street
Bath
BA1 1HE

Visit
www.hometownworld.co.uk

Follow us @hometownworldbooks

MIX
Paper from
responsible sources
FSC® C023419

Hometown World